Start Reading 4

Derek Strange

OXFORD UNIVERSITY PRESS

The flower

1 Five hundred years ago, a young girl called Devi lived in a town in the mountains in India. Her family's house had a big garden. Sometimes Devi and her friends had picnics or played games together there.

2 Sometimes she sat and read her book under the trees. There were some beautiful trees in the garden, but one was Devi's special tree.

3 Devi's tree was taller than the other trees. It was more beautiful than the other trees. It had long brown branches and big green leaves. Devi watched the birds and she listened to the wind in her tree. But there were never any flowers on the tree.

4 Every year Devi waited for a flower. All the other trees had flowers on them, but there were not any flowers on her tree. She was sad.

5 Devi lived in the same house for eighty years. She was now an old woman. But every evening she walked through the garden to see her tree. Every evening she looked for a flower.

6 One evening she arrived at the tree and saw one beautiful pink and yellow flower near the top of the tree. No flower in the garden was more beautiful than that flower. Devi smiled. She was very happy.

7 She walked back through the garden and went into the house. The door closed. Devi did not walk in the garden again.

Exercises

A True or false?

1 Devi wrote letters under the trees.
2 There were many special trees in Devi's garden.
3 Devi's special tree was tall and beautiful.
4 Devi's tree had beautiful flowers on it every year.
5 Every evening Devi looked for a flower on her tree.

B Finish the sentences.

waited	lived	saw	had	were

1 Devi __________ in a house with a very big garden.
2 There __________ some beautiful trees in Devi's garden.
3 Sometimes she __________ picnics with her friends in the garden.
4 Every year she __________ for a flower on her special tree.
5 One evening she __________ a very beautiful flower on the tree.

C Write the words in the squares.

1 Devi's special tree was very . . . .
2 It had big green . . . .
3 There was one flower near the . . . . of the tree.
4 She listened to the . . . . in her tree.
5 The tree had long brown . . . .
6 She walked through the . . . . every evening.
7 There was one very beautiful . . . . on the tree.

A fireman's day

1 Terry King is a fireman. He works at a fire station in London. The fire-engines are at the fire station and Terry's special boots and trousers are always in his fire-engine.

2 Terry starts work in the afternoon. He and the other firemen clean their fire-engines every day. One man sits near the telephone. He can answer it quickly, all day and all night.

3 Sometimes Terry sleeps for a short time in the night. There are some beds in a room at the fire station. Terry sleeps there – he wears all his clothes in bed! Firemen can always get to fires very quickly.

4 The alarm bell is ringing! There is a fire in a big hotel. The firemen are going to fight the fire now! Terry gets up and runs to his fire-engine. He puts on his coat and he picks up his yellow helmet.

5 All the firemen climb into the fire-engine and Terry drives it out of the fire station.

6 At the hotel, the firemen see some people at a window. They cannot jump down and the fire is getting near them. The firemen put up the long ladders and Terry climbs up to the window. He is going to help the people. They can climb down the ladder.

7 Now all the people are safe. The firemen are going to go into the hotel. They are going to fight the fire.

Exercises

A Read and match.

1 Terry King is . . .
2 The firemen clean . . .
3 Terry goes to work . . .
4 He sometimes sleeps for . . .
5 He always wears . . .

. . . in the afternoon.
. . . all his clothes in bed.
. . . their fire-engines every day.
. . . a fireman in London.
. . . a short time in the night.

B Answer the questions.

1 Where does Terry King work?
2 When does he start work every day?
3 Where does he sometimes sleep for a short time?
4 The alarm bell rings. What does Terry do?
5 What do the firemen put up to the windows of the hotel?

C Look at this picture. Write the numbers.

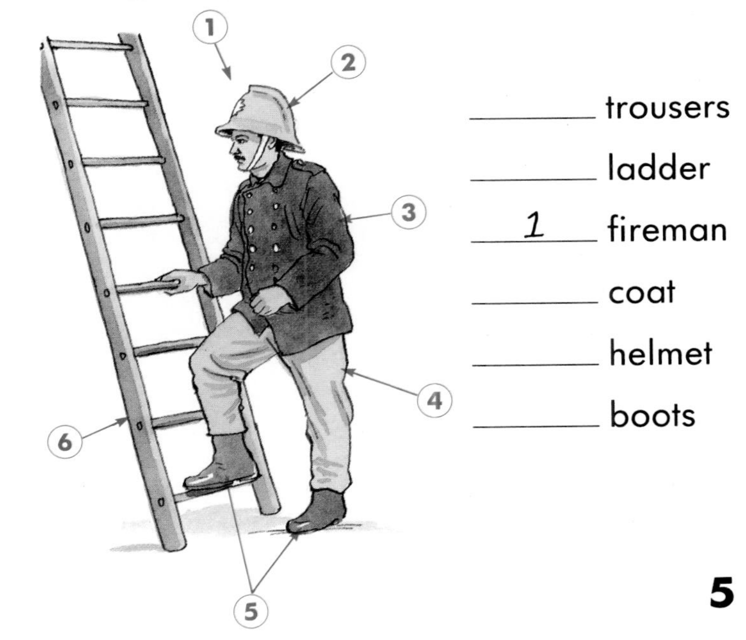

______ trousers
______ ladder
___1___ fireman
______ coat
______ helmet
______ boots

Taffy's trousers

1 Taffy was a thief. Jake was a thief, too.
One day Jake saw some pictures in the newspaper.
'There are some diamonds in one of the rooms of the big house on the hill,' Jake said. 'Let's go to the house tomorrow night. Let's steal the diamonds!'
'Good idea!' said Taffy. 'We're going to be rich!'

2 The next night, in the garden of the big house, they waited very quietly. A woman came out and drove away in her car.

3 'Come on!' whispered Jake. 'But be careful – there's a big dog in the house.'
They opened one of the windows carefully. They climbed into the house and they went upstairs quietly. They saw the box of diamonds and took it.

4 'It's heavy,' said Taffy loudly.
'Sh! Don't shout! Whisper!' said Jake.
Jake climbed out of the window and waited outside. Taffy had the box.

5 The dog heard the thieves and woke up. It barked loudly. Taffy dropped the box of diamonds. He jumped through the window, but the dog got a big piece of his trousers.

6 Taffy and Jake ran away quickly. But the dog had the piece of Taffy's trousers in its mouth. Later, the police came and they took the piece of his trousers to the police station.

7 The next day Taffy had a new piece on the back of his trousers. But a policeman saw Taffy's trousers.

'Taffy,' he said, 'I want to ask you some questions . . .' And he showed Taffy the old piece of his trousers. Taffy looked at it sadly.

'Oh no!' he said. He was a very stupid thief.

Exercises

A Answer the questions.

1 (Picture *1*) Where were the diamonds?
2 (Picture *2*) Who came out of the house and drove away?
3 (Picture *3*) How did Taffy and Jake get into the house?
4 (Picture *4*) Who climbed out of the window first?
5 (Picture *6*) Who had a big piece of Taffy's trousers?
6 (Picture *7*) Who saw the new piece on the back of Taffy's trousers?

B Write sentences.

1 Jake / saw / picture / diamonds / newspaper
2 opened / windows / carefully
3 took / box / diamonds
4 dog / piece of / trousers
5 policeman / new piece / back of / trousers

C Finish the sentences.

carefully	quietly	quickly	loudly

1 Jake and Taffy waited in the garden very ______________.
2 They opened a window at the back of the house ______________.
3 'It's heavy!' said Taffy ______________.
4 Taffy and Jake ran away from the house ______________.

Only £29.99!

**The new SCOUT 16K is a clock and a calculator, an address book and a diary.
The SCOUT 16K is the new pocket computer for you!**

Do you ever wake up late?

Put the **SCOUT 16K** beside your bed and go to sleep. The **SCOUT** wakes you up at the right time in the morning.
The **SCOUT**'s clock tells you the time and the day and the date, too!
The **SCOUT 16K** is your alarm clock!

Do you sometimes forget your family's birthdays?

The **SCOUT 16K** can remember sixteen birthdays for you.
When are you going to buy some flowers for your mother? When are you going to send a card to your brother? The **SCOUT** can tell you.
When are you going to go to the dentist's? The **SCOUT** can remember the date for you.
The **SCOUT 16K** is your desk diary!

Do you usually forget people's telephone numbers?

You can 'write' your friends' and your family's addresses and phone numbers on your **SCOUT 16K**. Then you can easily find them and 'read' them again later.
The **SCOUT 16K** is your address and phone book!

Do you sometimes make mistakes in your sums?

You can always find the right answers quickly with your **SCOUT 16K**.
The **SCOUT 16K** is a clever little calculator, too!
The **SCOUT 16K** is the pocket computer for your work at the office, at school and at home.

Only £29.99!

The **SCOUT 16K** costs only £29.99!

Buy now!

Buy your SCOUT 16K today!

Visit our shop at 18 Cinema Street, London EC2 or telephone 988 7000.

Exercises

A True or false?

1. You can put the SCOUT 16K into your pocket.
2. The SCOUT 16K cannot tell you the day and the date.
3. The SCOUT 16K can tell you the dates of people's birthdays.
4. The SCOUT 16K can write letters for you.
5. The SCOUT 16K can do sums for you quickly.

B Answer the questions.

1. Where can you see and buy the new SCOUT 16K?
2. Where can you use the SCOUT 16K?
3. How many birthdays can the SCOUT 16K remember for you?
4. What is the address and telephone number of the SCOUT 16K shop?
5. How much does the SCOUT 16K cost?

C Read and match.

1. You write 'HAPPY BIRTHDAY' on . . .
2. You do sums on . . .
3. You write days and dates of birthdays in . . .
4. You write people's house numbers and streets in . . .
5. You find people's names and phone numbers in . . .

. . . an address book.
. . . a diary.
. . . a phone book.
. . . a card.
. . . a calculator.

Oceanauts

1 The sea

There is a lot of water on Earth. The sea covers three quarters of the surface of Earth. The land covers one quarter. What is in the sea? What is on the floor of the sea?

2 Submarines

Three hundred years ago an Englishman made the first diving machine, and two hundred years ago an American made the first submarine. Today machines can dive deeper and can stay under the water longer. Thirty years ago a small American submarine dived 11,000 metres under the sea!

3 'Oceanauts' and their work

'Astronauts' explore space in spaceships; 'oceanauts' explore the sea and its floor in submarines. Oceanauts are brave scientists. They are making maps of the floor of the sea. They drive special small tractors there. They are exploring the mountains, the rocks and the valleys on the floor of the sea. Some of the rocks under the sea give us useful metals. We can find and pump out oil and gas from the floor of the sea.

4 Towns under the sea

Oceanauts can now also live in special buildings under the sea. They are planning small towns on the floor of the sea, with stations for their submarines and garages for their sea tractors.

5 Food from the sea

The sea gives us food, too. Many people eat fish and some people eat seaweed. Scientists are now farming the fish and some of the plants in the sea. They are using the sea carefully and well. But this is a beginning. We can explore the world under the sea and learn a lot more.

Exercises

A Match the questions with the answers.

1. Is there a lot of water on Earth?
2. Do oceanauts explore space in spaceships?
3. Are there a lot of useful things under the sea?
4. Can we pump out oil from the floor of the sea?
5. Are scientists planning towns under the sea?

Yes, they are.
Yes, there is.
Yes, we can.
No, they do not.
Yes, there are.

B Make sentences.

1. is / lot / Earth / water / . / on / a / There / of
2. ? / on / floor / sea / the / is / the / of / What
3. . / Oceanauts / of / can / the / floor / the / on / drive / sea
4. planning / the / under / . / small / sea / towns / are / They
5. are / They / the / carefully / using / . / sea

C Write the words in the squares.

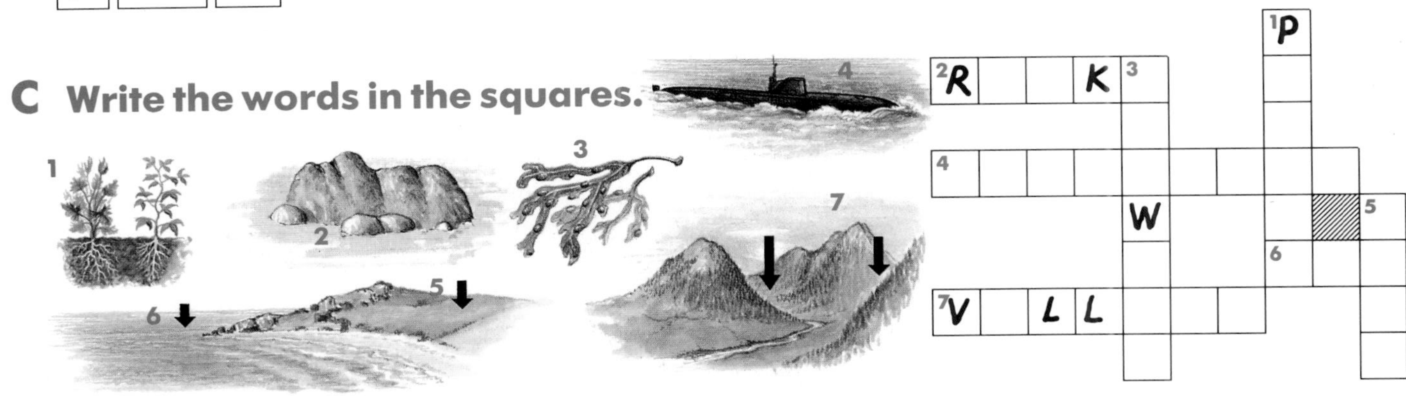

Three postcards

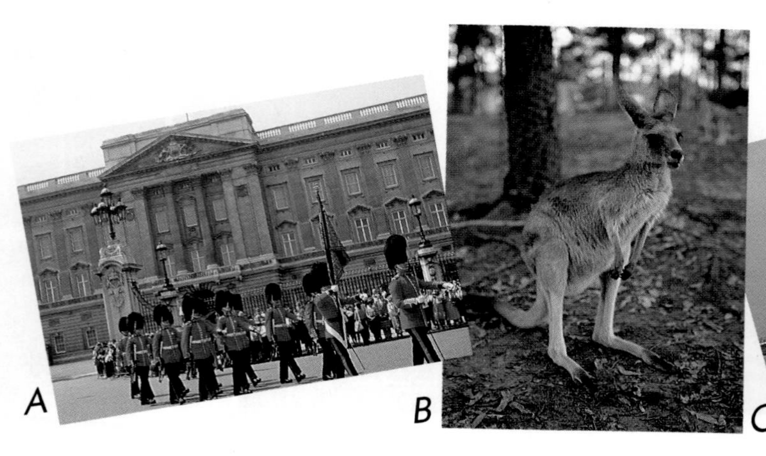

A B

C

Sydney, 4th July.

Sydney is beautiful! It is winter here now, but the weather is not cold. It is warm and sunny. I am sitting in a park in the middle of Sydney. People are having picnics on the grass near me.

Yesterday I went by ferry across the harbour to the zoo. It is a very good zoo and I saw some 'Big Red' kangaroos. They are very tall. This afternoon I am going to see the famous Sydney Opera House.

See you soon.
Love, Sandy.

Jane Brown,
3 New Road,
Oxford.
OX1 4LE.
England.

1

London, 4th July.

London is wonderful! There are some very beautiful old buildings here. Our hotel is an old grey building near a big park. I have a photo of it to show you. Yesterday was sunny, but today it is raining. Last night there was a storm and some branches fell off the trees in the park. My hat flew away in the wind.

This morning we saw the soldiers in their red coats outside Buckingham Palace - that's the Queen's home in London. This afternoon we are going to do some shopping.

Will you send my love to your grandparents, please?

Lots of love, Mother.

Miss Kate Nixon,
201 Madison Street,
New York.
NY 10016.
USA.

2

New York, 4th July.

New York is great! I arrived here two days ago and I am staying in a good hotel near Central Park. Today is Independence Day in America. It is hot and sunny. All the people have American flags in their hands or on their hats or on their cars. The children all have red, white and blue balloons with stars on them. Everyone is smiling and happy.

This afternoon I am going to go across the harbour and am going to see the Statue of Liberty.

Love, Judy.

Mr. T. Green,
10 Forest Road,
London.
NW 10.
England.

3

Exercises

A Match the postcards with the pictures.

1 Postcard *1*
2 Postcard *2*
3 Postcard *3*

A 

B 

C 

B Answer the questions.

1 (Postcard *1*) What is the weather like in Sydney?
2 (Postcard *2*) What is the weather like today in London?
3 (Postcard *2*) Who usually lives in Buckingham Palace?
4 (Postcard *3*) What is the special name for the Fourth of July in America?
5 (Postcard *3*) What is the weather like in New York?

C Write the dates.

1 *The Fourth of July, 1989.*
2 ______________________
3 ______________________
4 ______________________
5 ______________________
6 ______________________

1 東京 4.7.89 TOKYO
2 NEW YORK 8.9.90 NEW YORK
3 LONDON 6.2.88 LONDON
4 SYDNEY 20.6.89 SYDNEY
5 9.4.89 CAIRO
6 ΑΘΗΝΑΙ 2.11.90 ATHENS

The gold of Acapetlan

1 Nico and Sam were on holiday with their parents in a small town near some of the ancient pyramids in Mexico.

2 One day they talked to a very old man in a shop in a small street of the town. The old man had very long white hair.

'My name is Acapetlan,' he said.

They became friends. The old man knew many wonderful stories about the history of the pyramids. He told them the story of the famous chief, Acapetlan the Great. He told them the story of the famous treasure, the lost gold of Acapetlan.

3 'Tomorrow I will show you the Pyramid of Acapetlan. Perhaps you will find the lost gold?' The old man smiled at his two young friends.

'The old man is Acapetlan the Great, I think,' Nico whispered to Sam loudly.

The old man heard him and smiled again. He said nothing.

4 The next day Nico and Sam walked with the old man to one of the pyramids near the town. Nico took a torch to the pyramids. He wanted to look for the gold!

The two boys wanted to climb up the pyramid and the old man waited for them below. They were near the top.

Suddenly Sam said, 'Look! A door.'

A small door opened in the side of the pyramid.

'Shall we go in?' asked Nico.

'OK,' said Sam. 'Come on.'

5 Nico turned on his torch and they went in. They came to some steps. The steps went down and down, into the middle of the pyramid.

6 The boys came to a big room. They stopped, their mouths open. In the middle of the room, on a gold chair, sat their friend, the old man, Acapetlan. He had a heavy gold crown on his head. There were gold cups, silver plates and diamonds near him in big boxes on the floor.

He looked at the two boys, but he said nothing. He smiled . . . and all the gold of Acapetlan sparkled in the room.

Exercises

A Put the sentences in order.

(   ) The old man knew wonderful stories about the pyramids.
(   ) In the middle of the pyramid there was a big room.
(1) Nico and Sam went to Mexico on holiday.
(   ) They found a door in the side of the pyramid.
(   ) The old man was in the big room on a gold chair.
(   ) The boys went to see the Pyramid of Acapetlan with the old man.
(   ) They met a very old man with white hair.

B Answer the questions.

1 Where did the two boys talk to the old man?
2 Where did the old man go with the boys?
3 What did Nico take to the pyramids?
4 Who saw the small door in the side of the pyramid?
5 What did the boys see near the old man in the big room inside the pyramid?

C Match the words with the meanings.

ancient	gold, silver and diamonds
crown	very interesting, very good
parents	very old
torch	say something very quietly
treasure	a small lamp with batteries
whisper → (say something very quietly)	mother and father
wonderful	kings and queens wear this on their heads

Looking after Sarah

1 Ben's baby sister, Sarah, is two. She is often naughty. Sometimes their mother asks Ben to look after the baby, and she goes out to the shops or to the Post Office for a few minutes. Ben always says 'Yes'. He likes to help his mother.

2 Last night Ben's mother and father wanted to go to his school for an hour to meet his teachers. They asked Ben to look after the baby. But Ben had a very difficult time.

He gave Sarah some toys to play with, and she was happy . . . for two minutes.

Then the telephone rang and Ben answered it.

'Hello? 94326 here.'

3 It was his friend, Mandy. She wanted to ask Ben about their homework, but Sarah wanted Ben to play with her. She started to cry.

'Sorry, Mandy. I can't hear you. Sarah's crying. She wants her ball to play with. Wait a minute . . .'

4 He put the phone down and found Sarah's big red ball. Sarah was quiet and Ben went back to the phone. But Sarah wanted to play, so she cried again, loudly.

'Sorry, Mandy. It's Sarah again. I think she wants something to eat now.'

'Give her a biscuit,' said Mandy.

Ben put the phone down and gave Sarah a biscuit. She ate it and was quiet.

But then Ben picked up the phone again and Sarah didn't like it. She started to cry again, very loudly now.

5 'Sorry, Mandy,' he shouted. 'I think Sarah wants something to drink now.'

'Don't shout! I can hear you! Give her some orange juice,' said Mandy.

So Ben gave Sarah some orange juice, and another biscuit, and a picture-book, and her doll, too. Then he went back to the phone. But Mandy wasn't there.

Ben decided to wait for his mother and father, and to phone Mandy again later. He wanted to talk about their homework quietly.

Exercises

A True or false?

1 Ben never likes to help his mother.
2 Mandy wanted to ask Ben about their homework.
3 Sarah wanted to play with Mandy.
4 Ben gave Sarah a big ball to play with.
5 Ben gave Sarah a biscuit to eat.

B Read and match.

1 Ben's mother and father wanted . . .
2 His mother asked Ben . . .
3 Sarah wanted Ben . . .
4 Mandy wanted . . .
5 Ben wanted . . .

. . . to play with her.
. . . to talk to Mandy quietly.
. . . to look after his baby sister.
. . . to meet Ben's teachers.
. . . to ask Ben about their homework.

C Finish the sentences.

a book	some orange juice	a picture	a toy	a biscuit

1 This is something to play with. It is ______________________ .
2 This is something to eat. It is ______________________ .
3 This is something to drink. It is ______________________ .
4 This is something to look at. It is ______________________ .
5 This is something to read. It is ______________________ .

World records

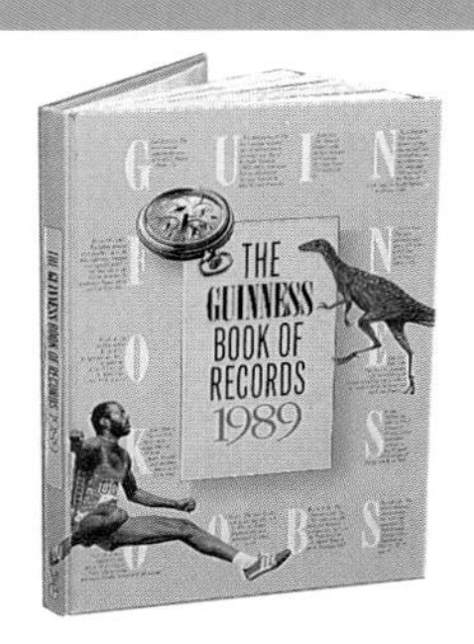

The *Guinness Book of Records* is the world's biggest list of records. It tells us the fastest and the strongest people in sports, the tallest and the shortest people or buildings, the fattest and the thinnest, the best and the worst in the world. All the records in the *Book of Records* are true. Some of them are interesting and some of them are funny. Here are some interesting questions and answers:

Question: How tall was the tallest person in the world?
Answer: He was 2 metres 72 centimetres tall. His name was Robert Wadlow. He lived in America.

Question: How heavy was the biggest cabbage in the world?
Answer: It was 55.7 kilograms.

Question: How old was the oldest person in the world?
Answer: He was Shigechiyo Izumi from Japan. He lived from 1865 to 1984 – that is 119 years!

(Perhaps there are older people than Mr. Izumi, but we don't know about them and they are not in the *Book of Records*.)

Question: What is the world's fastest ball game?
Answer: Baseball? No. Tennis? No. It is the Spanish game of 'pelota'. The fastest ball in 'pelota' travelled at more than 300 kilometres an hour!

There is a new *Book of Records* every year. Every year people try to break old records and make new ones.

For example: How much spaghetti can one person eat, and how quickly? The record now is 62 metres of spaghetti in 21 seconds! But this man is trying to break the old record. Look at all that spaghetti! Will he be in the new *Book of Records* next year?

Exercises

A Answer the questions.

1 How tall was Robert Wadlow?
2 How big was the biggest cabbage in the world?
3 How old was Mr. Shigechiyo Izumi?
4 How much spaghetti did somebody eat to make a world record?
5 How often is there a new *Book of Records*?

B Write sentences.

1 Robert Wadlow / tallest / in the world
2 Shigechiyo Izumi / oldest / in the world
3 biggest / cabbage / world / 55.7 kilograms
4 fastest / ball game / world / 'pelota'
5 Every year / people / new / records

C Look at this picture. Answer the questions.

1 Who is the tallest? *Anna is the tallest.*
2 Who is the shortest? ____________
3 Who is the youngest? ____________
4 Who is the oldest? ____________
5 Who is the fattest? ____________
6 Who is the thinnest? ____________

Anna

Beryl

Carol

Len's parrot

1 Len's shop was famous. In the shop there was a beautiful and clever parrot. His name was Dewey. Dewey helped Len in his shop: he knew all the customers and he always said 'Good morning' or 'Good afternoon' to them. He spoke more politely than Len!

2 Sometimes Len left the shop for a few minutes and Dewey looked after it. Dewey stood on the counter and spoke to the customers.

'Please wait a minute,' he said. 'Len will come back soon.'

The customers waited or they came back later. They all knew Len and Dewey.

3 One day Len went to the bank. Dewey stood on the counter and watched the door.

Suddenly a big grey cat came in. Dewey was very frightened.

He started to fly up to the top of the door quickly, but his wings knocked some bottles of expensive oil onto the floor. The bottles broke and the cat ran away.

Len came back from the bank. He opened the door and saw the oil on the floor. He was very angry.

'You stupid bird!' he shouted at Dewey. 'Get out of my shop! Go away!'

4 Dewey did not say a word. He flew out of the window and sat in a tree. He waited. He was very unhappy.

The next day Len was not angry. He wanted to go to the Post Office, but Dewey was up in the tree.

'I'm sorry, Dewey,' Len said. 'Please come back and look after the shop for me.'

Dewey did not say a word. He flew down from the tree and stood on the counter. Len went out to the Post Office.

5 After a few minutes the door opened and some customers came in.

Suddenly a voice shouted: 'Fire! Fire! Get out of this shop as quickly as you can!' It was Len's voice!

All the customers ran out of the shop, into the street.

They shouted 'Fire! Fire!', and after a few minutes the fire-engines came.

But there was no fire in the shop – only Dewey, on the counter. He was looking happier again now.

Len and all the customers laughed.

Exercises

A True or false?

1. Len had a clever parrot in his shop.
2. Dewey sometimes looked after the shop.
3. Dewey always shouted loudly at the customers.
4. Dewey knocked the bottles onto the floor with his wings.
5. Len shouted 'Fire! Fire!' to the customers.

B Put the sentences in order.

( ) A big grey cat came into the shop. Dewey was frightened.

( ) The next day Dewey shouted at some customers.

( ) Len saw the oil on the floor. He shouted at Dewey.

(1) Len had a clever parrot called Dewey.

( ) Dewey knocked some bottles of expensive oil off the counter.

( ) Len went to the bank and Dewey looked after the shop.

C Find words.

____

____

____

____

____

k a n g r y g q j b f
s f h p n c l e v e r
f a m o u s s t w a i
v w k l r k t j q u g
p v j i s t u z i t h
n q u t k r p u j i t
e x p e n s i v e f e
k r m v u j d w v u n
s q n a u g h t y l e
u n h a p p y k z p d

____

____

____

____

____

Picture dictionary

an address book | an alarm bell | angry | a baby | a balloon

barking | a boot | a branch | a cabbage | a calculator

a coat | a computer | a crown | crying | a customer

a diary | driving | dropping | expensive | a ferry

a flag | funny | laughing | grey | a harbour

heavy | a helmet | a hill | India | jumping

a kangaroo | leaves | a list | meeting | metals

a mistake | orange juice | parents | a parrot | a picture-book

pink | a post office | a postcard | a pump | a pyramid

rich | sad | seaweed | a soldier | spaghetti

a torch

toys

treasure

whispering

a wing

Irregular verbs

		have	had	say	said
come	came	hear	heard	see	saw
eat	ate	know	knew	sit	sat
fly	flew	leave	left	stand	stood
get	got	read	read	take	took
go	went	run	ran	wake	woke

A year

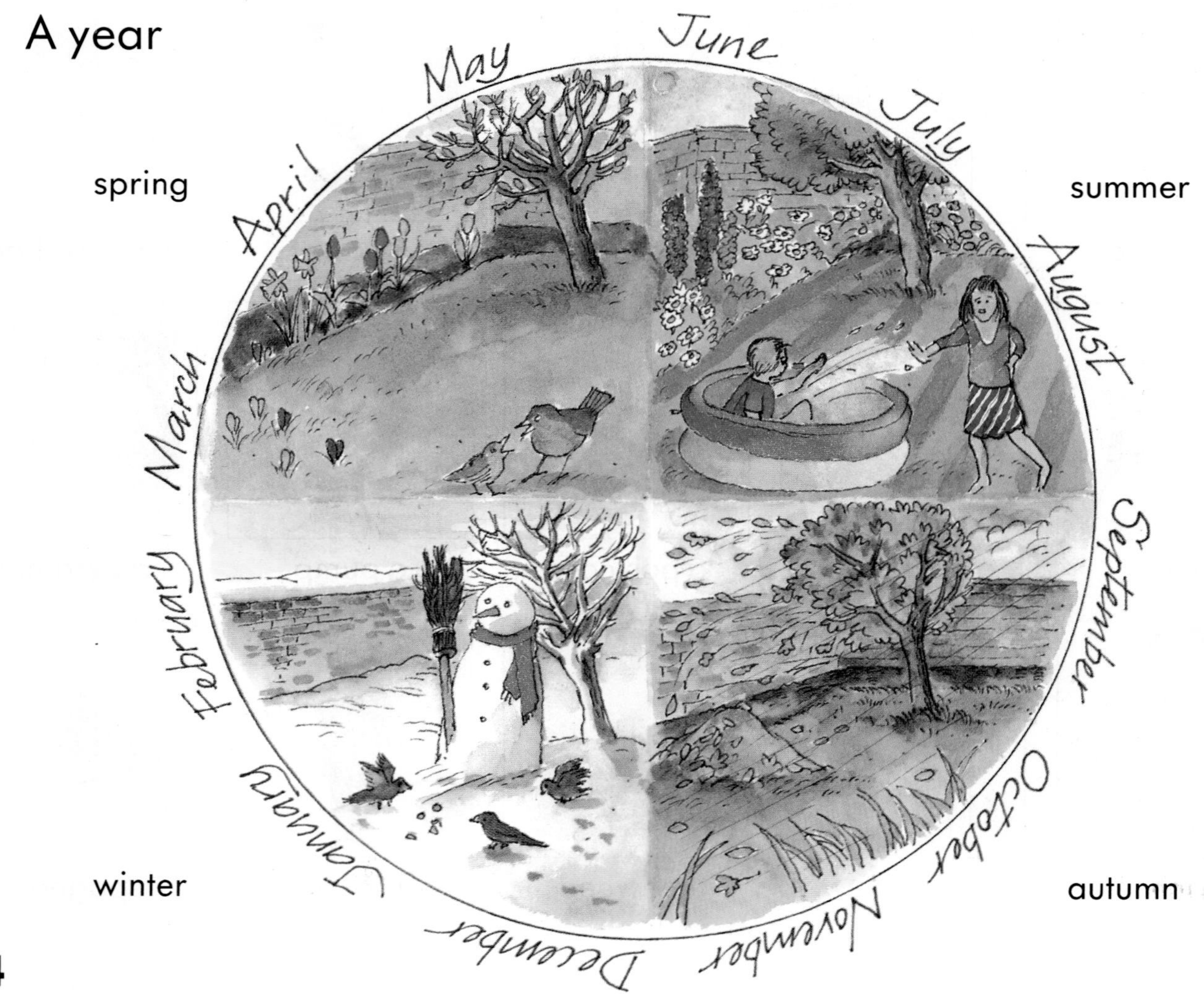